The COW That Laid an Egg

For the gorgeous Katinka

And for Georgie and Albie too, for putting up with me – A.C.

To Archie Harold

With love, Harold and Jeannie

First
published in hardback in
Great Britain by HarperCollins
Children's Books in 2007. First
published in paperback in 2008.
ISBN 13: 978-0-00-717968-8
7   9   10   8   6
HarperCollins Children's Books is a
division of HarperCollins Publishers Ltd.
Text copyright © Andy Cutbill 2007
Illustrations copyright © Russell Ayto 2007
The author and illustrator assert the moral right to be
identified as the author and illustrator of the work.
A CIP catalogue record for this title is available from the British
Library. All rights reserved. No part of this publication may be
reproduced, stored in a retrieval system, or transmitted in any form
or by any means electronic, mechanical, photocopying, recording or
otherwise, without the prior permission of HarperCollins
Publishers Ltd, 77-85 Fulham Palace Road, Hammersmith,
London W6 8JB. Visit our website at:
www.harpercollins.co.uk
Printed in China

The COW That Laid an Egg

HarperCollins *Children's Books*

by Andy Cutbill

illustrated by Russell Ayto

Marjorie the cow felt
down in the dumps.
"What's wrong, Marge?"
clucked the chickens.

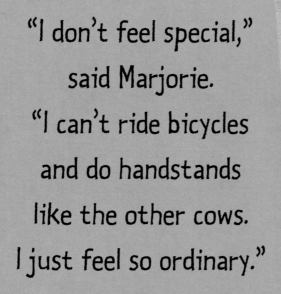

"I don't feel special,"
said Marjorie.
"I can't ride bicycles
and do handstands
like the other cows.
I just feel so ordinary."

The following morning
there was an almighty commotion
in the barnyard.

"I've laid
an egg!"

shrieked Marjorie.

All the other cows
were astonished.
None of them had ever
laid an egg before.

Even the farmer came running.
"Oh, my goodness!" he cried.
"Marjorie's laid an egg!"

The farmer's
wife called the
local newspaper.

People came
from far and wide.

"We're extremely proud of Marjorie," announced the farmer to the crowd.

Marjorie felt much
more special now.
And the chickens were
as pleased as Punch too.

But the other cows weren't so happy.

"We don't think you
laid that egg,"
the cows said to Marjorie.
"We think the crafty
chickens did it."

Marjorie felt shocked.

"prove it,"

said the chickens.

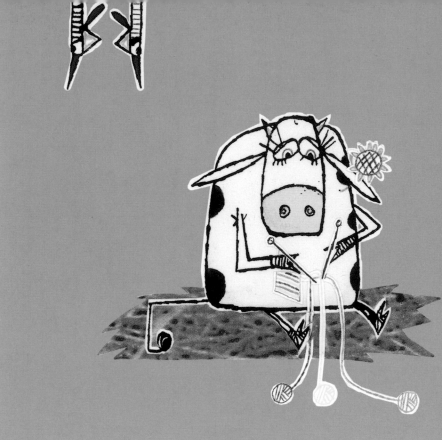

So they all waited for the egg to hatch. Day after day they watched,

as Marjorie sat on the egg to keep it warm. But nothing happened.

Until suddenly, one morning,
they heard a noise.

TaP taP taP

"Here it comes!" shouted
one of the cows.

And as Marjorie stood up...

tap tap tap

the egg

cracked

open

and out

hopped

a small, brown,

feathery bundle.

"There," said one of the cows, nodding. "A **Chicken!**"

Suddenly, the tiny creature looked up at Marjorie.

OOOOOO!""

it said loudly.

Marjorie smiled and held her baby tight.
"A cow," she said.

And she promptly named it Daisy.